Tim has a nap.

Tim is in the mud.

1

A big bug sat on top
of Tim.

The bug bit him.

Tim is mad at the bug.

Tim got up.

The bad bug had bit him.

Tim ran to nip it.

The bug is on the
big log.
Tim ran to it.

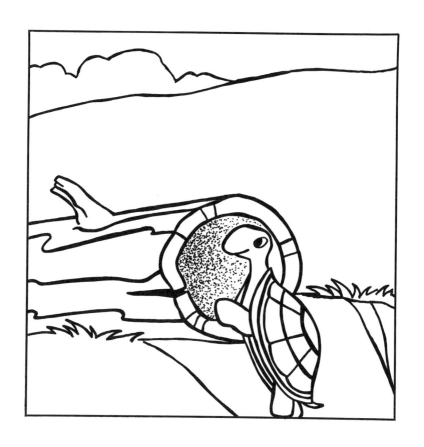

The bug hid in the log.

Tim got up, but Tim can not fit in it.

Tim got up on the log.
The bug is not in the
log.

The log is big, but it did tip.

Tim can not sit on it.

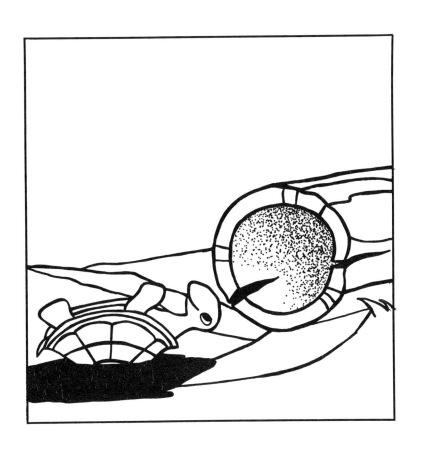

Tim can not sit up.

Tag ran up to Tim.

Tag can not tip
him up.

The pup ran on.

10

It is hot in the sun.

Tim is hot and sad.

Al ran up to Tim.

Al is big.

Al can tip him up.

Al had to tug on Tim.

Tim got a big tug.

Al got him to sit up.

Tim has a pal.

His pal is Al.

Tim and Al ran to

the mud.

Tim and Al sat in the mud.

Tim and Al had a lot of fun.